Africa   America   Asia   Australia

Contents

This story is from South Africa.
Many people in South Africa
live in the country, a long way from the city.
They travel by bus to buy the things they need.
The buses get very crowded with people,
packages, sacks of potatoes, bags of grain,
live chickens, and even goats!
When people have to wait a long time
for the buses to come,
the bus stops get very busy.

What a Commotion!

Written by Merle-Anne Braithwaite
Illustrated by Philip Webb

It was very hot in the street.

Jabulani's father said,
"Look after the goat, Jabulani.
I will go and buy a drink for us."

Across the street from the bus stop
was a sign, *KWAMKHIZE – FOOD AND DRINK.*
Jabulani's father went to get the drinks.

2

Jabulani looked at the goat.
The goat's yellow eyes were nearly shut.
She was very hot. A fly buzzed
near her head. She flicked one white ear.
Jabulani looked for a place to tie up the goat.
There was a wire bin at the bus stop.
Jabulani tied the rope to the wire.

"That's a fine goat," said an old man
who was waiting for the bus.

"Such a fine animal," said a woman
who was sitting in the shade.

3

Jabulani bent down to look for bottle tops.
He didn't see the green weeds
growing out of the cracks in the road.
But the goat saw the weeds.
She pulled and pulled at her rope.
Weeds are good food for a goat!
She pulled and pulled
and the wire bin fell over.
The wire bin fell onto the road!

The goat's yellow eyes opened wide.
She took off down the street.

"Your goat, your goat!" shouted the old man
who was waiting for the bus.

"She's running away," shouted the woman
who was sitting in the shade.

"Oh no!" said Jabulani as he ran after the goat.
"Stop her! Stop her!" Jabulani shouted.

The goat ran through the fruit stalls.
The fruit rolled onto the road.
People ran to get out of the way.

What is
the setting and
the mood of
this story?

5

Screech! A taxi stopped!
The driver shouted at the goat
that had run onto the road.

Crash! A car crashed into the back of the taxi.
The drivers got out and shouted at each other.

Everyone was shouting!

At last, the wire bin got stuck on a post,
and the goat came to a stop.

Jabulani ran to the goat.

"It's all right," Jabulani said.

What is the problem in this story? What do you think will happen?

The goat backed away. She was frightened.
Jabulani held the rope.
Now Jabulani was frightened.
He was frightened
of what his father would say.
He was frightened
of what the people at the fruit stalls would say.
He was frightened
of what the taxi driver would say.
He held onto the rope
and bent down by the goat.
He patted her on the head.
That was how Jabulani's father found them.

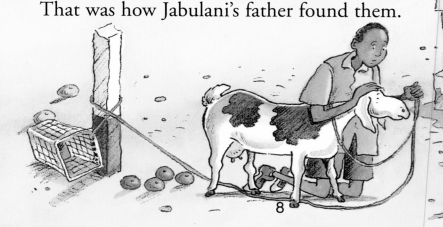

8

"Jabulani! Jabulani! What a commotion!"
said his father.

Jabulani hung his head.

"I'm sorry, Baba," he said.

Were you right?

His father started to laugh.

"What a commotion!
People will be talking about Jabulani
and his goat for a long, long time," he said.

Jabulani got up.
Jabulani and his father went back to the bus stop.

This time, Jabulani did not let go of the rope!

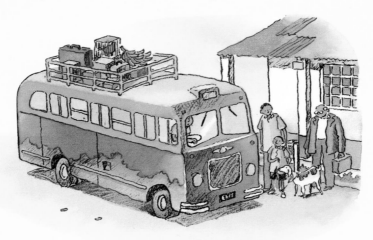

America

This story is from
the United States of America.
Harriet Powers made her quilts
more than one hundred years ago.
People still make quilts today.
Quilts often have a story to tell!

Quilts

The Quilts of Harriet Powers

Written by Sharon Capobianco
Illustrated by Marjorie Scott

Harriet Powers was born in 1837.
She lived most of her life
in Athens, Georgia.

Harriet Powers could not read or write,
but she did learn to sew.
When Harriet Powers was young,
she was taught how to make quilts.
She sewed the stories
that she had heard into her quilts.

Who do you think would have taught Harriet Powers to make quilts?

In 1886, the people of Athens, Georgia, had a fair. At the fair, there was a tent for people to show things they had made. Some people showed their best fruits and vegetables. Some people showed jams and jellies that they had made. And some people showed their sewing. Harriet showed one of her quilts at the fair.

An art teacher named Jennie Smith was at the fair. She wanted to buy Harriet's quilt, but Harriet didn't want to sell it.

What do people do at fairs, today?

13

One day Harriet found she needed some money,
so she had to sell her quilt.
But by then, Jennie didn't have the money
to buy the quilt.
It took Jennie a year
to save up the five dollars
to buy the quilt.

Harriet made another quilt.
It took Harriet more than three years to make it.
People think that this quilt was shown at
the Nashville Exhibition of 1898.
Some women liked the quilt very much.
The women wanted to buy the quilt.
They wanted the quilt
to give to the Reverend Charles Hall
of Atlanta University.

When Jennie Smith died in 1946,
the quilt that she had bought for five dollars
was given to the Smithsonian Institution
in Washington, D.C.
The quilt is now in the National Museum
of American History.

Harriet's quilt for the Reverend Hall
is in the Museum of Fine Arts
in Boston, Massachusetts.

Why do you think
it took Harriet so long
to make a quilt?

How to Make a

Written by Sandra Iversen   Illustrated by Clare Bowes

To make a friendship quilt, you will need eight friends
to work with.

You Will Need

- ❏ 9 squares of cotton fabric
  each 12 inches x 12 inches (30 cm x 30 cm)

- ❏ pieces of felt

- ❏ felt-tip marker

- ❏ scissors

- ❏ pins

- ❏ needles and thread

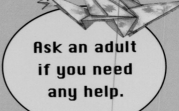

Ask an adult
if you need
any help.

- ❏ fabric to put on the back of the quilt
  The fabric should be
  36 inches x 36 inches (90 cm x 90 cm).

- ❏ wooden rod 36 inches (90 cm) long

- ❏ 4 pieces of ribbon
  each 24 inches (60 cm) long

Friendship Quilt

How to Begin

- ❏ Take one of the squares of cotton fabric and some felt.
- ❏ Think about the picture you would like to put on your cotton square.
- ❏ Draw this picture on pieces of felt.

- ❏ Cut out your picture and pin it onto the square.

- ❏ Now sew your felt picture onto the cotton square.

Putting the quilt together

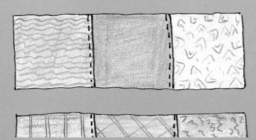

❏ Sew all the cotton squares together.

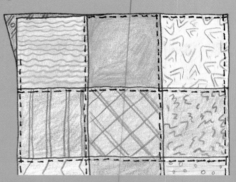

❏ Pin the backing fabric to the cotton squares, with right sides together.

❏ Sew both layers of fabric together around the edges. Leave a small gap to pull the fabric through.

❏ Turn the fabric to the right side and sew up the small gap.

❑ Sew the ribbons to one side of the quilt
and tie the ribbons over the wooden rod.

Hang up your friendship quilt for all your friends to see.

People in Asia
use paper to make lots of things.
Even tigers!

The Paper Tiger

Written by Michael Moreu
Illustrated by Marie Low

2

1 inches

She made a paper inchworm
to crawl along the floor.
With squares of bright clean paper,
she began to make some more.

Here
I come!

Bird chases the worm!

She made a paper bird
   to eat the paper worm.
And then a paper cat,
   to chase the bird in turn.

A paper dog was next
   to chase away the cat.
And then a paper horse,
   not too thin and not too fat.

She made a paper monkey
   to ride upon the horse.
And bear and hare and twenty mice,
   she lost count, of course.

She made a paper tiger
to chase them all away.
It raged and roared and grumbled,
so the animals would not stay.

But that hungry paper tiger,
   with its mighty paper paws,
thought that she was good to eat
   and chased her with its claws.

Help!
Tiger! Tiger!

She tried to tell her parents,
   she showed her paper cuts,
but her mother rolled her eyes
   and said, "No ifs, no ands, no buts."

No one listened to her story
   or the tiger's grumbling wail.
And only little bits were left
   of the paper tiger's tail.

Australia

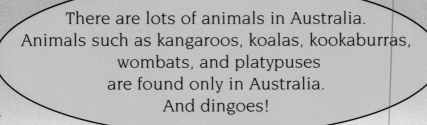

There are lots of animals in Australia.
Animals such as kangaroos, koalas, kookaburras,
wombats, and platypuses
are found only in Australia.
And dingoes!

A Drink
for Darby Dingo

Written by Richard Maloney
Illustrated by Kelvin Hawley

Darby was a dingo.
He liked the moonlight.
Some nights he howled at the moon.

And Darby liked rain, too.
It had rained all day.
The rain had cooled the ground,
and the air was cooler, too.

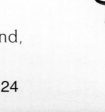

24

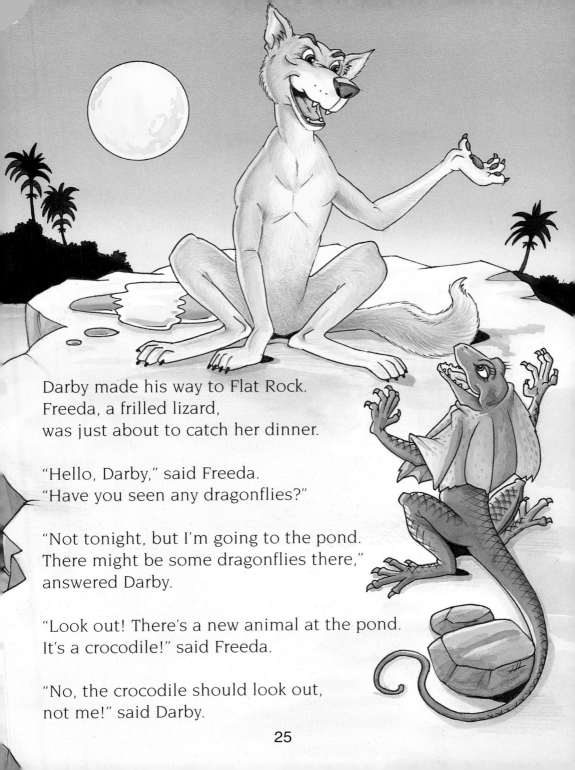

Darby made his way to Flat Rock.
Freeda, a frilled lizard,
was just about to catch her dinner.

"Hello, Darby," said Freeda.
"Have you seen any dragonflies?"

"Not tonight, but I'm going to the pond.
There might be some dragonflies there,"
answered Darby.

"Look out! There's a new animal at the pond.
It's a crocodile!" said Freeda.

"No, the crocodile should look out,
not me!" said Darby.

Darby came to some large trees.
Kim, a koala, was sitting on a branch.

"Hello, Darby," she said.
"What is the moon like tonight?
I can't see through all the leaves."

"Hello, Kim. The moon is big tonight.
It's like gold. I'm going to the pond
for a cool drink," answered Darby.

"Look out at the pond," said Kim.
"There's a new crocodile down there."

"That crocodile better look out for me!"
said Darby.

Just then Rodney, a red kangaroo,
jumped out of the trees.
He was going very fast.

"Slow down, Rodney. What's the rush?"
asked Darby.

"Hello, Darby. There's a big…"
said Rodney.

"I know, I know. There's a big crocodile
down by the pond," said Darby.

"No," said Rodney, "he's just behind you!"

Darby turned around.
Two yellow eyes were looking at him.

Find out
some more things
about Australia.

Snap! The crocodile snapped at Darby.

"Hello, crocodile," said Darby.

The crocodile snapped again!
Darby jumped out of the way.
The crocodile had pulled hairs from his tail!

"You look a bit thin," said Darby.
"Have you had your dinner yet?"

The crocodile looked at Darby.

"I've just passed a nest of kookaburra eggs. They would be much easier to get than me," said Darby.

"Where?" asked the crocodile.

"Over there. Over the side of the cliff," said Darby.

What is going to happen next?

The crocodile moved very fast. "Where?" he asked.

"You'll have to get closer," said Darby.

29

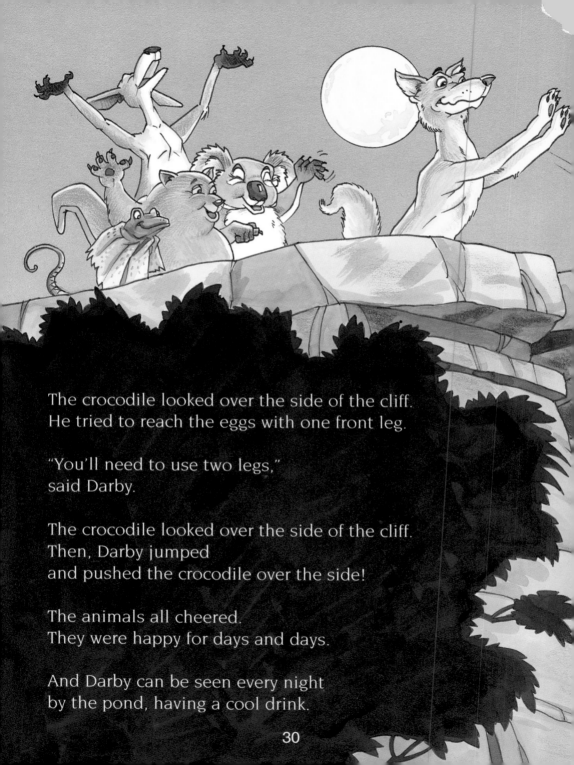

The crocodile looked over the side of the cliff.
He tried to reach the eggs with one front leg.

"You'll need to use two legs,"
said Darby.

The crocodile looked over the side of the cliff.
Then, Darby jumped
and pushed the crocodile over the side!

The animals all cheered.
They were happy for days and days.

And Darby can be seen every night
by the pond, having a cool drink.

WILDCATS
Bobcat

Glossary

🐾 **commotion** – a lot of noise

🐾 **dragonflies** – insects with long, thin bodies and four wings that live near freshwater

🐾 **exhibition** – a place where people can go to see things that people want to show

🐾 **inchworm** – the larva of a moth that moves in loops

🐾 **koala** – a slow bearlike animal of Australia with thick fur

🐾 **kookaburra** – a bird of Australia with a cackling call

🐾 **The Smithsonian Institution National Museum of American History** – a museum that shows things from the history and cultures of the North American people

🐾 **South Africa** – a country in southern Africa